It's another great book from CGP...

This book is bursting with brain-teasing practice questions that'll put your
Chemistry skills to the test at Key Stage Three (ages 11-14).

It's ideal if you're working at foundation level — it covers what would
have been called Levels 3-6 in the old (pre-2014) Curriculum.

We've even included a **free** Online Edition you can read on your computer or tablet!

How to get your free Online Edition

Just go to **cgpbooks.co.uk/extras** and enter this code...

3136 1769 8794 4457

By the way, this code only works for one person. If somebody else has used
this book before you, they might have already claimed the Online Edition.

CGP — still the best! ☺

Our sole aim here at CGP is to produce the highest quality books —
carefully written, immaculately presented and dangerously close to being funny.

Then we work our socks off to get them out to you
— at the cheapest possible prices.

Contents

Section 1 — Classifying Materials

Section 2 — Chemical Changes

Section 3 — The Earth and The Atmosphere

Published by CGP

Compiled by Paddy Gannon

Editors:
Gordon Henderson
Sean Stayte
Charlotte Whiteley
Sarah Williams

With thanks to Jamie Sinclair and Karen Wells for the proofreading.

ISBN: 978 1 78294 138 5

Groovy website: www.cgpbooks.co.uk

Jolly bits of clipart from CorelDRAW®
Printed by Elanders Ltd, Newcastle upon Tyne.

Solids, Liquids and Gases

Q1 Complete these sentences by circling the correct word in the brackets.

a) There are (**no** / **two** / **three**) states of matter.

b) Solids, liquids and gases have (**different** / **the same**) properties.

c) (**Solids** / **Liquids** / **Gases**) have a definite shape.

d) Liquids change (**shape** / **density**) depending on the container they're in.

e) (**Solids** / **Liquids** / **Gases**) don't flow.

Q2 Write **solid**, **liquid** and **gas** in the correct spaces on the arrow to show the differences in their **density**.

high density   medium density   low density

....

Q3 Read the sentences and then write down which **state of matter** is being described.

a)
> It has a definite shape and volume.
> Materials in this state aren't easily squashed.

State: ....

b)
> This state of matter flows easily. It always
> has the same volume as the container it's in.

State: ....

c)
> Materials in this state flow easily. They have
> a definite volume and are hard to squash.

State: ....

Q4 Which state of matter is the most **compressible**? Circle the correct answer.

Solid   Liquid   Gas

Particle Theory

Q1 Write **true** or **false** next to each sentence to show whether it is correct or not.

a) All materials are made up of tiny particles. ....

b) The arrangement of particles doesn't affect the properties of a material. ....

c) Liquids are easy to squash. ....

d) Liquids are usually quite dense. ....

Density means how heavy something is for its size.

e) Gases are easy to squash as there's lots of space between the particles. ....

Q2 Tick (✔) the correct boxes about particles in **solids**, **liquids** or **gases**.

	Particles are close together	Particles are free to move
Solid		
Liquid		
Gas		

Q3 Match each of the pictures on the left with the **correct arrangement** of particles on the right (**X**, **Y** and **Z**) by drawing a line between them.

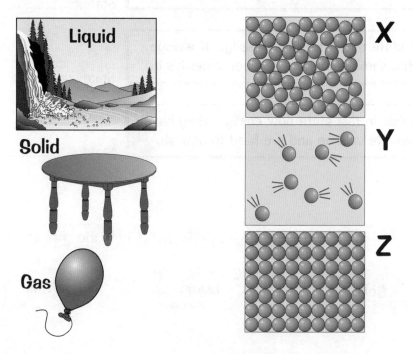

Particle Theory

Q4 The **particles** in solids, liquids and gases are **arranged** in different ways.

a) In which state of matter are the forces between the
particles the **strongest**? Circle the correct answer.

solid   liquid   gas

b) Complete this sentence.

> The .... the forces between
> the particles, the further apart the particles will be.

Q5 A **liquid** is poured into the first container, and then into each of the others, one at a time.

a) Does the liquid's volume remain the same each time? ....

b) Does the height of the liquid remain the same each time? ....

Q6 If you tip a watering can filled with water, water will **flow** out of the
spout. Explain how the particle arrangement of water means it can flow.

....

....

....

Particle Theory

Q7   Fill in the missing words about particles in a **solid**.
Words may be used once, more than once, or not at all.

same	close	compact	dense	air	fast	move
squashed		vibrate	volume		flow	small

In a solid, the particles are held very .... together,

although they do .... a bit. The particles can't

.... very much, so all solids keep the ....

shape and .... and can't .... like liquids.

Solids can't easily be .... because the particles are already

very .... together. Solids are usually .... ,

as there are lots of particles in a .... volume.

Q8   This question is about a **gas**. Look at the picture below and put a
tick (✔) next to the phrases that are true about the particles in steam.

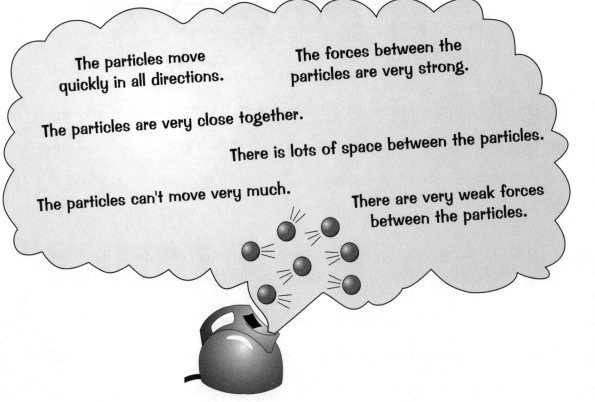

More Particle Theory

Q1 Which **two** of the properties of a material's particles will change when a material changes state? Circle the correct answers.

| The arrangement of the particles | The type of particles | The energy of the particles |

Q2 This diagram shows how a substance can change from one **state** to another. Pictures A, B and C show the **particles** in different states of matter. The arrows show how one state can **change** into another.

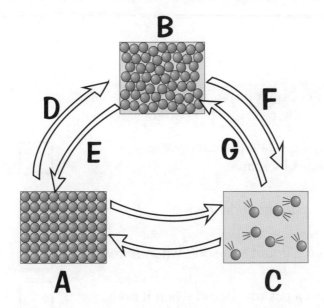

a) A, B and C show the particles in three **states** of matter.
Write the name of the correct state next to each letter below.

A — ....

B — ....

C — ....

b) Name the **types of change** shown by arrows D, E, F and G.
The first one has been done for you.

D — **melting**

E — ....

F — ....

G — ....

6

More Particle Theory

Q3 Use the words below to fill in the gaps in this paragraph.

gain   weaker   temperature   gas   faster   boiling

When a liquid is heated, the particles .... energy. This makes

the particles move .... This makes the forces between the

particles .... At a certain .... , the

particles have enough energy to break the forces between them and the liquid

turns into a .... This is called ....

Q4 Read these sentences about **physical changes**.
Put a tick (✔) in the box next to each correct sentence.

a) When materials change state the energy
of the particles always increases.

b) Condensing is the opposite of dissolving.

c) Water changes from a liquid to a solid when it freezes.

d) Water changes from a gas to a liquid when it boils.

e) When a liquid freezes into a solid, heat is given out.

f) Heat must be supplied to a liquid to turn it into a gas.

g) When a liquid freezes, the forces
between the particles get stronger.

HINT: Freezing is the opposite of melting.

Q5 Circle all of the physical changes below that can happen when **heat is supplied**.

melting   condensing   freezing   boiling

Section 1 — Classifying Materials

More Particle Theory

Q6   Sylvan took some **butter** out of the fridge and **heated** it in a pan.

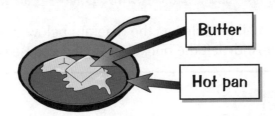

Butter

Hot pan

a)   When the **solid** butter is heated, what happens to the **particles**? Circle the correct answer.

They lose energy.   **They get more energy.**   **They lose mass.**

b)   Tick (✔) any sentences that are **true** about a solid being heated.

☐ The particles move faster, so the forces holding the particles together get weaker.

☐ The particles move faster, so the forces holding the particles together get stronger.

☐ The particles move slower, so the forces holding the particles together get stronger.

☐ The particles move slower, so the forces holding the particles together get weaker.

c)   Eventually Sylvan saw the butter **melt**.

i)   What happens to distance between the **particles** in the butter as it melts?

....

ii) What happens to the energy of the particles in the butter as it melts?

....

Q7   Circle the correct words in brackets to complete this paragraph about **diffusion**.

The spreading out of (**particles** / **heat**) is called (**compression** / **diffusion**).
A smell spreading across a room is an example of this effect. The smell
particles move from where there are (**none** / **lots**) of them to where there
are (**fewer** / **more**) of them.

More Particle Theory

Q8   Andy has left a bucket of **smelly** cheese porridge to cool down. Dagmar is sitting at the other side of the room. After a while, Dagmar can smell the porridge.

   a) Draw some more smell particles on the diagram below to show where the smell particles would be **just after** Andy left the bucket of smelly cheese porridge in the room.

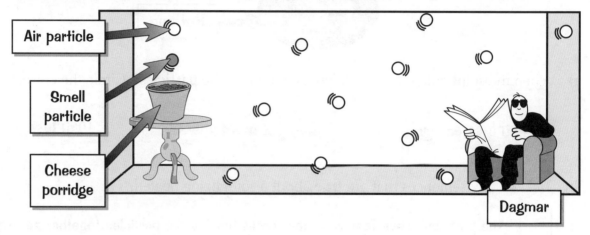

   b) Which of the **three** diagrams below shows where the smell particles would be after the smell of porridge had diffused in the air? Put a tick (✔) in the correct box.

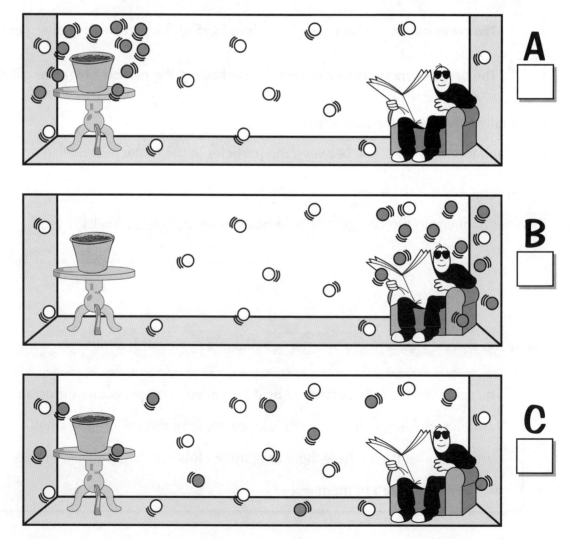

Atoms and Elements

Q1 Draw lines to match up the beginnings and ends of these sentences about **atoms** and **elements**. One has been done for you.

Elements are substances that...

...the symbols for all the elements.

Everything on Earth...

...contain only one type of atom.

Each element has...

...one or two letters.

The symbol for an element is made up of...

...is made up of atoms.

Atoms are pretty much...

...a name and a symbol.

The periodic table contains...

...the smallest, simplest types of particle.

Q2 Put a tick (✔) next to all the things below that are **elements**.

Carbon ☐   Nitrogen ☐

Air ☐   Carbon dioxide ☐

Uranium ☐   Water ☐

My pet hamster ☐   Helium ☐

Atoms and Elements

Q3 This huge word search contains the names of **thirty elements**. Find them and cross them off the list at the bottom of the page as you go. One has been done for you.

```
I O D I N E N N V M U I S S A T O P
R C F Z S A L Z P S B R E V L I S E
O U Q M L I C N I Z Y F A X U V W D
N U S A M L L U E C H L O R I N E I
S M R H U L L I T P N U G O K L L X
U U M U I C L A C I H O F F L M T O
L I L O I J E H R O J R S E E R I R
F L B P A L K G J S N I D D A S N E
U E I H Y D R O G E N C C D T E P
R H C O Y U R M M N O E Z A U P G P
F E M S D A R G J K N B B W R C Y O
E Y U P R N L I T H I U M V T B X C
A R I H O O I K C H I U M B B B O A
G U N O X G N E F A N E G O R T I N
O C A R Y R E E G U C R I H O O P O
L R R U P A L U M I N I U M D K F R
D E U S O D I U M N N M D L Y V A O
A M U I S E N G A M U I L L Y R E B
```

~~Hydrogen~~	Fluorine	Chlorine	Tin
Helium	Neon	Argon	Iodine
Lithium	Sodium	Potassium	Gold
Beryllium	Magnesium	Calcium	Mercury
Boron	Aluminium	Iron	Lead
Carbon	Silicon	Copper	Uranium
Nitrogen	Phosphorus	Zinc	
Oxygen	Sulfur	Silver	

Atoms and Elements

Q4 The diagram below shows the **periodic table**.

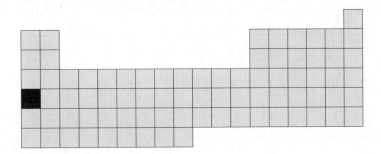

a) What is listed in the periodic table?

....

b) In the periodic table, what is a **group**?

....

c) The periodic table has **eight** groups. Label each group
with the correct number on the diagram above.

d) In the periodic table, what is a **period**?

....

e) One square in the periodic table above has been coloured in black.
Is the element that is normally listed in this square a **metal** or a **non-metal**?

....

Q5 The pictures below show the **atoms** in substances A - I.
Circle the substances that are **elements**.

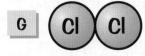  

Atoms and Elements

Q6 Use a copy of the **periodic table** to help you answer the questions below.

a) Write down the names and symbols of **four** elements with a **single letter** symbol which is the **same** as the **first letter** of the element's name. The first one has been done for you.

1. **Boron (B)**

2. ....

3. ....

4. ....

b) Write down the names and symbols of **two** elements with a **single letter** symbol which is **different** to the **first letter** of the element's name. The first one has been done for you.

1. **Tungsten (W)**

2. ....

c) Write down the names and symbols of **three** elements with **two-letter** symbols, where both letters are the **same** as the first two letters of the element's name. The first one has been done for you.

1. **Aluminium (Al)**

2. ....

3. ....

I'm just nipping out to buy some copper

Cu soon

d) Write down the names and symbols of **three** elements with **two-letter** symbols, where both letters are **different** to the first two letters of the element's name. The first one has been done for you.

1. **Iron (Fe)**

2. ....

3. ....

e) In the periodic table, find an element whose symbol and name have the **same** first letter, but a **different** second letter. Write down the element's name and symbol.

....

Atoms and Elements

Q7 Give the names of the elements represented by the following **symbols**:

a) O ....

d) Cl ....

b) Al ....

e) Na ....

c) Ca ....

f) F ....

Use a periodic table to help you.

Q8 These pictures show the arrangement of atoms in **aluminium**, **iron** and **oxygen**. Look at the diagrams and then tick (✔) the sentence below that is correct.

Aluminium   Iron   Oxygen

☐ None of the substances are elements because they all contain more than one atom.

☐ All of the substances are elements because they each contain only one type of atom.

☐ Oxygen isn't an element because it has two atoms joined together.

Q9 Using a copy of the periodic table, pick the **odd one out** for each of the lists **a)** to **f)** and **explain why** it's different from all the others.

Hint: Look at which groups and periods the elements are in.

a) Magnesium, aluminium, sodium, silicon:— ....

b) Ca, Cu, Cl, Cs:— ....

c) Cl, Br, O, I:— ....

d) Helium, argon, hydrogen, krypton:— ....

e) Li, Na, K, Fe:— ....

f) Lithium, nitrogen, oxygen, carbon:— ....

Atoms and Elements

Q10 **One** of these sentences about the Periodic Table is incorrect.

a) Put a cross (✗) next to the sentence that is **incorrect**.

> Elements in the same group have similar properties to each other. ☐
>
> Elements in the same period have similar properties to each other. ☐

b) **Rewrite** the sentence that you crossed so that it is **correct**.

....

....

Q11 Sheena has samples of sodium, potassium and lithium. The samples have got mixed up and she doesn't know which one is which.

a) Which group of the Periodic Table are all these elements in?

....

b) Give **two** properties of the elements in this group.

1. ....

2. ....

c) In general, do the **properties** of the elements change or stay the same as you go **down** a group?

....

d) How does the reactivity of the elements change as you go down this group?

....

e) Sheena knows that all the elements in this group react with water. She drops each sample in water. Write the **name** of each element below the **description** of its reaction.

> It fizzes a lot and catches fire.   It fizzes a lot.   It fizzes a bit.

....

Compounds

Q1 Many compounds are made up of **molecules**.

a) Circle the **two true** sentences below about compounds and molecules.

> There must be atoms of at least two different elements in a compound.

> Molecules are formed when atoms join together.

> Molecules are formed when atoms break apart.

> There must be at least two atoms of the same element in a compound.

b) What is a **join** between atoms called?

....

Q2 Divide the following into **elements** and **compounds** by writing them on the correct lines below.

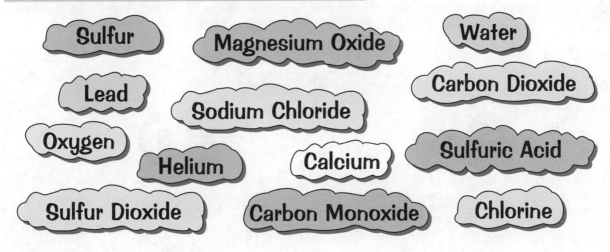

Sulfur   Magnesium Oxide   Water
Lead   Sodium Chloride   Carbon Dioxide
Oxygen   Helium   Calcium   Sulfuric Acid
Sulfur Dioxide   Carbon Monoxide   Chlorine

Elements

....

....

Compounds

....

....

16

Compounds

Q3 The diagrams below show the **particles** in three different substances. Each colour shows a different type of atom.

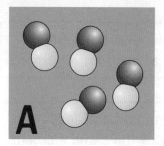 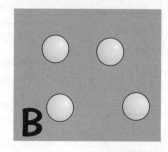 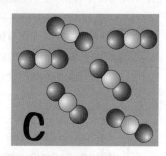

a) Which picture(s) show(s) particles in a **compound**? Explain your answer.

....

....

b) Which picture(s) show(s) an **element**? Explain your answer.

....

....

Q4 Write the **chemical formula** of these **molecules**.

a)

....

b)

....

c)

....

d)

....

e)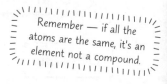

....

f)

....

Remember — if all the atoms are the same, it's an element not a compound.

Section 1 — Classifying Materials

Compounds

Q5 Look the **chemical formula** for each compound below and write down the names of the **elements** it contains.

a) FeS ....

b) NaCl ....

c) CO ....

Q6 The chemical formula of a compound tells you how many **atoms** of each **element** it contains. Using the formula, write down the **number** of...

a) ...sodium atoms in sodium chloride (NaCl). ....

b) ...oxygen atoms in copper sulfate ($CuSO_4$). ....

c) ...hydrogen atoms in sulfuric acid (H_2SO_4). ....

Q7 When the elements **iron** and **sulfur** are mixed together and heated, they **react** to make a compound called **iron sulfide**. Iron is magnetic, but iron sulfide isn't. Look at the diagram and then circle the correct words in the brackets below.

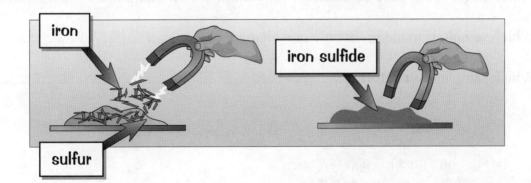

In a (**chemical reaction** / **mixture**), chemicals join together or split apart to

form new (**substances** / **elements**). When elements (**split apart** / **combine**)

like this, they form new (**atoms** / **compounds**). Compounds produced in a

chemical reaction will have (**exactly the same** / **different**) properties to the

original elements. For example, (**sulfur** / **iron**) is magnetic. When it reacts with

(**sulfur** / **iron sulfide**), it makes (**sulfur** / **iron sulfide**) which (**isn't** / **is**) magnetic.

Mixtures

Q1   What is a **pure substance**? Tick (✔) the correct answer.

☐ A substance made up of only one type of element or one type of compound.

☐ Two or more substances that are chemically joined up.

☐ Two or more substances that are not chemically joined up.

☐ A mixture.

Q2   These pictures show the **particles** in three different samples, **A, B** and **C**.

Sample A   Sample B   Sample C

a) Which samples are **pure substances**? ....

b) Which sample is made up of only one **element**? ....

c) Which sample is a **mixture**? ....

Q3   Tick (✔) the box next to each sentence to show whether it is **true** or **false**.

		True	False
a)	Mixtures can be made by dissolving a solid in a liquid.	☐	☐
b)	A mixture has the chemical properties of the substances it is made from.	☐	☐
c)	Air is a pure substance.	☐	☐
d)	Mass is lost when one substance is dissolved in another.	☐	☐
e)	It is easier to separate the substances in a mixture than in a pure substance.	☐	☐

Section 1 — Classifying Materials

Mixtures

Q4 Lucy has a beaker that contains a **compound** made up of two elements and a beaker that contains a **mixture** of the same two elements.

a) What is a mixture?

....

....

b) Would it be easier to **separate** the mixture or the compound into elements? Explain your answer.

....

....

Q5 The sentences below are definitions of words to do with **dissolving**. Fill in the gaps to complete each word.

A solid being dissolved is called a s __ __ __ t e.

A liquid that a solid is being dissolved into is called a s __ l v __ __ __.

The mixture of a dissolving solid and liquid is called a s __ l __ __ i o n.

A solid that will dissolve is called __ __ __ __ b l e.

A solid that won't dissolve is called __ __ s o l __ __ __ __.

Q6 Dora dissolves salt in a beaker of water.
Describe how Dora can get the **solid salt** back again.

....

....

Mixtures

Q7 Bryony adds salt to a beaker of water to make a **solution** of salt water.
She stirs the mixture until the salt has completely disappeared.

a) Complete this sentence.

The salt has not vanished, it has been .... in the water.

b) What happens to the **bonds** holding the salt together when it mixes with the water?

....

c) The picture below shows the water particles in the solution.
Complete the picture by drawing **empty circles** to show the **salt** particles in the solution.

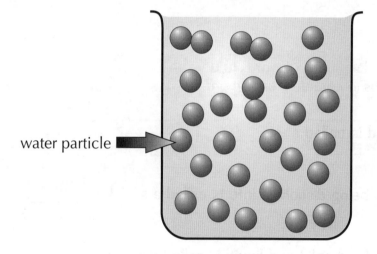

water particle

Q8 Abid has a beaker of water that's **full to the brim**.
He dissolves a spoonful of **sugar** in the water.

a) The water **doesn't overflow** from the beaker
when Abid adds the sugar to the water. Explain why.

....

Hint: Have a look at the water
particles in Q7 c). Where could the
sugar particles go?

....

b) Abid added 4 g of sugar to 80 g of water.
What was the **mass** of the sugar solution? Circle the correct answer.

76 g   80 g   4 g   84 g

Separating Mixtures

Q1   Eoin has a tub of **rock salt**. Rock salt is a **mixture** of two compounds — salt and sand.

a)   What **difference** between salt and sand allows them to be **separated**?

....

b)   The **four** steps of a method Eoin could use to separate rock salt are shown below.
     Put them in the correct order by writing the numbers **1-4** next to each label.

DISSOLVING

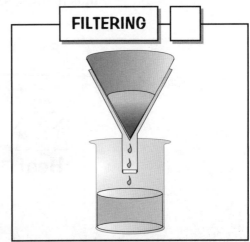

FILTERING

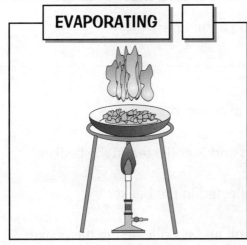

EVAPORATING

GRINDING

c)   In the filtering step, why does the **sand** collect on the filter paper?

....

....

d)   Why doesn't the **salt** collect on the filter paper?

....

e)   What is **left behind** in the evaporating dish after the evaporating step has finished?

....

Separating Mixtures

Q2   Byron was told that **saltwater** is made by mixing solid **salt** and liquid **water**. He
tested this theory by using the apparatus below to **separate** a sample of saltwater.

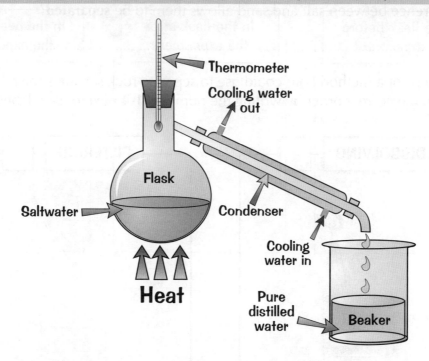

After heating the saltwater for a while he found that **pure water** collected in the beaker.

a) What is the name of this method of separating a mixture?

....

b) Tick (✔) the statement that is **true** about this experiment.

  ☐ The salt in the saltwater boils off and is collected in the beaker.

  ☐ The saltwater boils off and is collected in the beaker.

  ☐ The water in the saltwater boils off and is collected in the beaker.

  ☐ The salt and water in the saltwater boil off and are collected in the beaker.

c) Why did he use a **condenser** in his experiment?

....

....

d) Name **one** other mixture Byron could get pure water from using this method.

....

Separating Mixtures

e) Draw the particles that would be in each place listed in the box below it.
I've drawn out particles of salt and water to help you.

In the flask before the experiment	In the flask after the experiment	In the beaker after the experiment

Salt particle ☐   Water particle ⬤

Q3   **Ink** is a mixture of several different dyes.

a) You can **separate** the dyes in ink using the steps below. The steps are in the wrong order. Write out the letters of the steps in the correct order below.

A. The solvent seeps up the paper, carrying the ink dyes with it.

B. You end up with a pattern of spots.

C. Draw a pencil line near the bottom of some filter paper.

D. Roll up the paper and put it in a beaker of shallow solvent.

E. The dyes will travel up the paper at different speeds.

F. Put spots of ink along the line.

Order: ...., ..., ..., ..., ..., ...

b) What is this method of separating mixtures called?

....

Section 1 — Classifying Materials

24

Separating Mixtures

Q4 Six students analysed **ink samples** from their pens in a Chemistry lesson. The pictures below show the analysis method and the **results**.

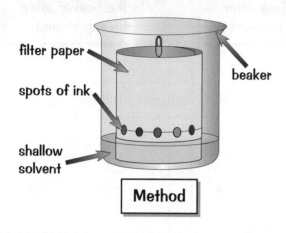

Method

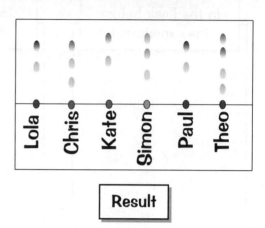

Result

a) **Circle** the **two** pupils that you'd expect to have the same ink in their pens.

Lola   Chris   Kate   Simon   Paul   Theo

b) Give a clear **explanation** of the reason for your answer to part **a)**.

....

....

....

Q5 Verity collected **muddy water** from a ditch. Back in her lab, she **distilled** the mixture to remove the mud and leave **pure water**. Then she measured the **boiling** point of the water to check that the water was pure.

a) She found that the water **boiled at 100 °C**. What does this tell you?

....

b) Reg did the **same** experiment and found that his water **boiled at 102 °C**. What does this tell you about the water that Reg distilled? Explain your answer.

....

....

Properties of Metals

Q1 Shade in the **Periodic Table** below to show where metals are found.

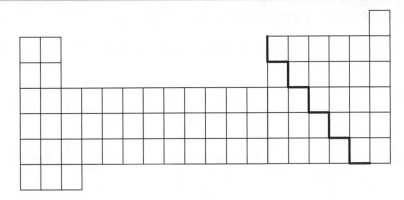

Q2 Saucepans are normally made out of **metal**. One reason for this is that metals have high **melting** and **boiling points**. Circle **one** other property of metals that makes them suitable materials to make saucepans from.

They are good conductors of heat.

They are shiny.

They are good conductors of electricity.

They have high densities.

They are sonorous.

LOBSTER POOL
Free Entry

Q3 Draw a ring around all the objects below that will be attracted to a **magnet**.

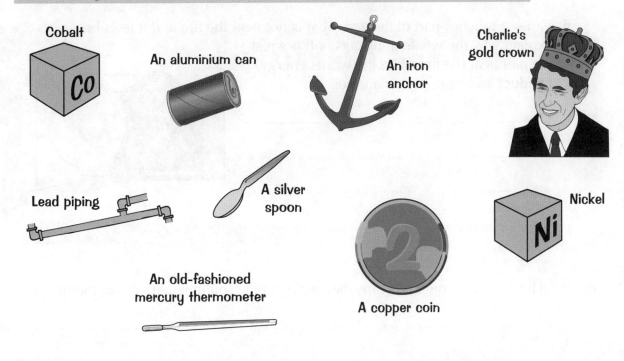

Cobalt

An aluminium can

An iron anchor

Charlie's gold crown

Lead piping

A silver spoon

Nickel

An old-fashioned mercury thermometer

A copper coin

Properties of Metals

Q4   Vanessa is a famous **gong** player. Her favourite gong is made from a metal called **brass**.

a)   Vanessa often **polishes** her gong to keep it **shiny** for concerts.

i)   What kind of **surface** does polished metal have? Tick (✔) the correct answer.

☐ spiky   ☐ fluffy   ☐ bumpy

☐ rough   ☐ smooth   ☐ see-through

ii) Why do polished metals look **shiny**?

....

b)   Vanessa left her brass gong next to a **fire** for a few hours.

i)   Circle the correct words in the brackets to complete the paragraph.

Although the fire made the gong very (**cold** / **hot**), the brass gong didn't melt because metals have (**high** / **low**) melting points. The atoms in metals are joined up with (**strong** / **weak**) bonds. That means a lot of (**sound** / **heat**) energy is needed to break the bonds between metal atoms.

ii) Vanessa touches part of the gong that is not near the fire and it feels hot. Explain why the whole gong gets hot, not just the part near the fire. Use the words **energy**, **conduct** and **heat** in your answer.

....

....

....

....

c)   Which property of metals means they make a nice **sound** when you hit them?

....

Properties of Metals

Q5 The wires in a plug are made from **metals**.

a) What name is given to the property of metals that allows them to be easily drawn into wires?

....

b) Give **one** other property of metals that makes them suitable for making plug wires.

....

c) Give **one** reason why **non-metals** are **not** used to make these wires.

....

d) Circle **one** part of a plug that should **not** be made of metal.

Pins that conduct electricity into the plug.

Casing that protects you from electricity flowing in the plug.

Screws that hold the bits of plug together.

Q6 Metals are used as **building materials** because they are **strong**, **tough** and **malleable**.

a) What does malleable mean?

....

b) Metals are also **very dense**. Tick (✔) the sentence that explains why this is.

☐ Metals are very dense because they have a lot of atoms in a small space.

☐ Metals are very dense because they have a few atoms in a small space.

☐ Metals are very dense because they have a few atoms in a large space.

Properties of Non-Metals

Q1 Here is part of the **Periodic Table** showing some **metals** and some **non-metals**. Use a pencil to shade in all the **non-metals**.

B	C	N	O	F	Ne
Al	Si	P	S	Cl	Ar
Ga	Ge	As	Se	Br	Kr
In	Sn	Sb	Te	I	Xe
Tl	Pb	Bi	Po	At	Rn

Q2 A party balloon is filled with a **non-metal gas**. It floats in the air. Which property of non-metal gases means it can float? Circle the correct answer.

| They have high densities | They are ductile | They have low densities | They are brittle |

Q3 Circle the correct words in brackets to complete the paragraph below.

> Non-metals have (**high** / **low**) melting points and
> (**high** / **low**) boiling points. This is because the forces
> which hold the particles together are very (**weak** / **strong**).

Q4 Circle any object(s) below that could be lifted out using the **magnetic** fishing rod.

Fishing for non-metals is really boron...

silicon chip   iron barrel   graphite pencil

Properties of Non-Metals

Q5   Look at the table below that describes two **different** balls.
The balls are made of either metallic or non-metallic **elements**.
For each, write down whether it's made of a **metal** or a **non-metal**.

	Colour	Weight	Magnetic
Ball 1	Dull red	Light	No
Ball 2	Shiny brown	Heavy	Yes

....

Q6   The "lead" in pencils is really a non-metal called **graphite**.

a)   What **element** is graphite?

....

b)   What happens if you try to **bend** the pencil?

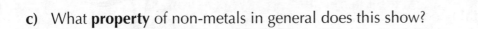

....

c)   What **property** of non-metals in general does this show?

....

d)   Circle the correct words in the brackets.

> The graphite in a pencil wears away (**quickly** / **slowly**).
>
> This is because the (**structure** / **magnetic field**) of
>
> graphite is (**strong** / **weak**) so the rough surface of the
>
> paper (**can't damage** / **scrubs away bits of**) the graphite.

Properties of Non-Metals

Q7   John investigated the **properties** of some **mystery substances**. The diagrams show the four tests (A – D) that he did on the substances. **Complete** the sentences below by filling in the blanks and circling the correct words in brackets.

a) **Test A** is testing ....
   ....

   The mystery substance in this test is probably

   a (**metal** / **non-metal**) because ....
   ....

b) **Test B** is testing ....
   ....

   The mystery substance in this test is probably

   a (**metal** / **non-metal**) because ....
   ....

c) **Test C** is testing ....
   ....

   The mystery substance in this test is probably

   a (**metal** / **non-metal**) because ....
   ....

d) **Test D** is testing ....
   ....

   The mystery substance in this test is probably

   a (**metal** / **non-metal**) because ....
   ....

Section 1 — Classifying Materials

Properties of Other Materials

Q1 Teacups are made from **ceramics**.

a) Write down **one** property of ceramics that makes them good for making teacups.

....

b) Explain your answer to part **a)**.

....

c) Give **one** other example of something that is made from ceramics.

....

Q2 **Polymers** are sometimes used instead of brass for making cheaper trombones.

a) Which of the following properties of polymers makes them good for making plastic trombones? Circle **one** correct answer.

Often flexible

Insulators of electricity

Strong but not heavy

b) Explain your answer to part **a)**.

....

c) Give **one** other example of something that is made from polymers.

....

Q3 Write the correct letter in each box to show whether each material is a **ceramic** (C) or a **polymer** (P).

Bone china ☐   Porcelain ☐
PVC ☐   Polythene ☐
Nylon ☐   Glass ☐

32

Properties of Other Materials

Q4 When the Space Shuttle returned to Earth, it got really **hot**. Why do you think the bottom of the Space Shuttle was covered in **ceramic tiles**? Tick (✔) the right box.

☐ Because ceramics are conductors of heat.

☐ Because ceramics are stiff.

☐ Because ceramics are insulators of heat.

☐ Because ceramics are insulators of electricity.

Q5 Boats are sometimes made from **fibreglass**, which is a **composite** material.

GLASS + POLYMER = FIBREGLASS

a) What is a **composite** material?

....

b) What is the main **advantage** of using composite materials?

....

c) Circle the correct words in the brackets to complete this paragraph.

> Fibreglass is made from (**glass** / **plastic**) fibres mixed into (**glass** / **plastic**).
> This means it has (**texture** / **properties**) of both materials. Fibreglass has a
> (**high** / **low**) density, like plastic, but it is very (**colourful** / **strong**) — like glass.

d) Write down **one** other thing made from fibreglass.

....

Section 1 — Classifying Materials

Properties of Other Materials

Q6 **Concrete** is often used as a building material.

a) What **type** of material is concrete?

....

b) Tick (✔) the **three** things that make up concrete.

Gravel ☐	Badgers ☐	Metal ☐
Sand ☐	Plastic ☐	Cement ☐

c) Why is concrete a **good** material to make buildings out of?

....

....

....

Q7 You have been asked to design a **kettle** which must have the features listed below.

New Kettle:

Feature 1 — Must be in the shape of a garden gnome.

Feature 2 — Must be easy to carry.

a) Read the list of features. Would you make the kettle out of **ceramics** or **polymers**?

....

b) Explain how your choice in part **a)** would help the kettle to have each feature.

Feature 1:...

....

Feature 2: ....

....

Section 2 — Chemical Changes

Equations

Q1 You can use **word equations** to show what happens in a chemical reaction.

a) Complete the sentence by circling the correct words in the brackets.

> In a chemical reaction, chemicals (**combine** / **split**) or
> (**combine** / **spilt**) to form (**new** / **old**) substances.

b) What is the general name for the chemicals **made** during a chemical reaction? Circle the correct answer.

reactants   products   acids   catalysts

c) Look at the word equation below.

> nitric acid + sodium hydroxide → sodium nitrate + water

Write down the names of the **two reactants** in this equation.

1. ....

2. ....

Q2 All elements have a **chemical symbol**.

a) What is the name of the table that lists all the elements and their symbols?

....

b) Tick the box next to the sentence below that is **true**.

The formula for a compound is made up of the symbols of the elements inside it. ☐

The formula for an element is made up of the symbols of the compounds inside it. ☐

c) Tick the box next to each symbol for an **element** below.

☐ H_2O ☐ C   ☐ H   ☐ Fe

☐ O   ☐ Na   ☐ CO   ☐ HCl

Equations

Q3 Chemical reactions are usually written using **symbol equations**.

a) The chemical formulas below are used in a lot of symbol equations.
Circle the correct name of each chemical next to each formula.

   i) CO_2 **carbon monoxide / carbon dioxide / calcium oxide / cobalt oxide**

   ii) NaCl   **nickel chloride / sodium carbonate / nitrogen chloride / sodium chloride**

b) The symbol equation below shows **sodium** and **water** reacting
together to make **sodium hydroxide** and **hydrogen**.

$$2Na + 2H_2O \rightarrow 2NaOH + H_2$$

   i) What is the chemical formula for a molecule of water?

   ....

   ii) How many sodium atoms are there at the start of this reaction?

   ....

   iii) How many hydrogen molecules are made in this reaction?

   ....

Q4 Geoff reacts **hydrochloric acid** and **sodium hydroxide**
together to make **sodium chloride** and **water**.

a) Circle the correct word equation below that shows this reaction.

   sodium hydroxide + water → sodium chloride + hydrochloric acid

   hydrochloric acid + sodium hydroxide → sodium chloride + water

   hydrochloric acid + sodium chloride → sodium hydroxide + water

   sodium hydroxide + water → hydrochloric acid + sodium chloride

b) Complete the symbol equation
below for this reaction.

   Hint: The formula for hydrochloric acid is HCl. The rest of
   the formulas you need are written elsewhere on this page...

   .... + ... $\rightarrow$ .... + ...

Chemical Reactions

Q1 Complete these sentences by circling the correct words in the brackets.

> Atoms (**are** / **are not**) made or destroyed in a chemical
>
> reaction. The atoms (**move around** / **all stay still**) during
>
> a chemical reaction and (**are** / **are not**) changed.

Q2 Muhammad is doing an experiment. He reacts **100 g** of **potassium iodide** with **100 g** of **lead nitrate**. They react to make **potassium nitrate** and **lead iodide**.

a) What is the **total mass** of the reactants in this reaction? Circle the correct answer.

| 10 g | 100 g | 200 g |

b) Muhammad mixes the potassium iodide and lead nitrate together as shown below.

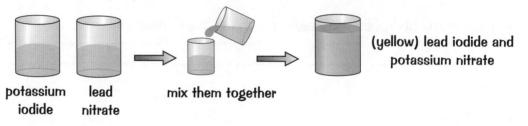

potassium iodide   lead nitrate   mix them together   (yellow) lead iodide and potassium nitrate

i) The reaction mixture turns yellow. A change in colour is just one change you can see during a chemical reaction. Suggest **one** other change you might see during a reaction.

....

ii) Muhammad says 'The colour of the reaction mixture changes. This shows new atoms have been made during the reaction'. Explain why he is **wrong**.

....

....

c) What do you know about the **total mass** of the products in this reaction?
Tick the box next to the correct answer.

It is more than the total mass of the reactants. ☐

It is the same as the total mass of the reactants. ☐

It is less than the total mass of the reactants. ☐

Examples of Chemical Reactions

Q1 What **three** things do you need for a **combustion** reaction to happen? Circle the correct answers.

Fuel

Heat

Carbon dioxide

Oxygen

Iron

Water

Copper oxide

Q2 David left an **iron nail** in the garden for a week. When he went to use it he found that it had **changed colour**.

a) What colour did the nail turn?

....

b) Complete the word equation for this reaction.

iron + oxygen ⟶ ....

c) Complete these sentences. The first letter of each missing word has been written for you.

The reaction of the nail and oxygen is an o.. reaction.

This reaction of iron and oxygen is also called r.. .

d) Where did the oxygen in this reaction come from?

....

Q3 Why is combustion so **useful**? Tick the box next to the correct answer.

Combustion releases energy. ☐

Combustion releases oxygen. ☐

Combustion releases water. ☐

Combustion releases carbon dioxide. ☐

Examples of Chemical Reactions

Q4 Car engines use **combustion** to release energy to power a car.

a) The petrol used in cars is made up of **hydrocarbons**.
Name the **two** elements that hydrocarbons contain.

1. ....

2. ....

b) Tick the box next to the word equation for the combustion of a hydrocarbon.

> hydrocarbon + water → carbon dioxide + oxygen ☐
>
> hydrocarbon + carbon dioxide → water + oxygen ☐
>
> hydrocarbon + oxygen → carbon dioxide + water ☐

c) Which of the following reactions is also an example of a combustion reaction?
Circle the correct answer.

| A bike rusting | Extracting a metal from a metal oxide | A bonfire |

Q5 The picture on the right shows a candle **burning in oxygen**.

a) What type of reaction occurs when something burns in oxygen?
Circle the correct answer.

| Thermal decomposition | Combustion | Rusting |

b) What **two** forms of energy are released by the burning of the candle?

1. ....

2. ....

c) The candle releases two gases when it is burning.
Name **one** of these gases.

....

Examples of Chemical Reactions

Q6 This question is about **oxidation** reactions.

a) What is **oxidation**?

....

b) Circle the oxidation reaction(s) below.

neutralisation   thermal decomposition   combustion

Q7 Susan heats a dish of **green copper carbonate**. After a while, the copper carbonate breaks down into **black copper oxide**.

Green   Black

Heat

a) Name this type of reaction.

....

b) Which gas is produced in this reaction? Tick the box next to the correct answer.

☐ Oxygen   ☐ Carbon dioxide   ☐ Hydrogen

c) Tick the box next to the correct sentence below.

☐ All substances break down when they are heated.

☐ Only certain substances break down when they are heated.

☐ Only liquids break down when they are heated.

d) Write a **word equation** for the reaction that turns copper carbonate to copper oxide.

....

More on Chemical Reactions

Q1 Adam put a piece of **magnesium** into some **acid** and watched the reaction. The **temperature** inside the test tube **increased** during the reaction.

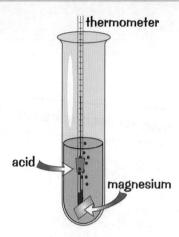

thermometer

acid

magnesium

a) Complete this sentence by circling the correct word in the brackets.

This reaction (**gave out** / **took in**) energy.

b) What form of energy was transferred between the reaction mixture and the surroundings?

....

c) Was this reaction endothermic or exothermic? Circle the correct answer.

endothermic   **exothermic**

Q2 Tick the correct box to show whether each of the following statements is **true** or **false**.

	True	False
a) Exothermic reactions give out energy to the surroundings.	☐	☐
b) Combustion is an endothermic reaction.	☐	☐
c) The temperature of an endothermic reaction mixture increases.	☐	☐
d) Energy is usually taken in or given out by a reaction as heat.	☐	☐

Q3 Circle the reaction below that is always **endothermic**.

oxidation   thermal decomposition   neutralisation

More on Chemical Reactions

Q4 Draw lines to match each example to the type of reaction it uses.

Hand warmers

Self-heating cans of coffee

Sports injury cold packs

A fire burning

Endothermic reaction

Exothermic reaction

Q5 Catalysts are used in industrial chemical reactions.

a) What is a **catalyst**? Tick the box next to the correct answer.

A catalyst is a substance that stops a reaction. ☐

A catalyst is a substance that speeds up a reaction. ☐

A catalyst is a substance that slows down a reaction. ☐

b) Complete the sentences using the words given below.

more   same   lower   cheaper

You can make .... product in the

.... amount of time by using a catalyst

in a reaction. Catalysts can also allow reactions to happen at

.... temperatures, which makes

reactions ....

c) Can catalysts be reused? Explain your answer.

....

....

42

Acids and Alkalis

Q1 For each item, decide whether it's **acidic**, **alkaline**, or if it's **neutral**. Write your answer in the box underneath each picture.

Q2 Look at the **pH scale** below.

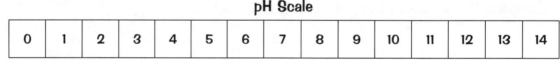

pH Scale

0	1	2	3	4	5	6	7	8	9	10	11	12	13	14

Draw lines to match each label on the left with the correct pH on the right.

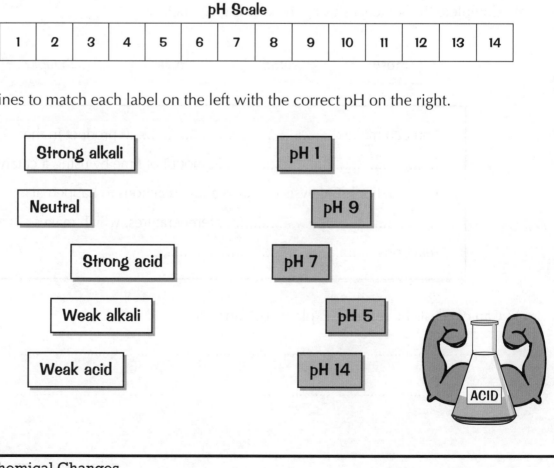

Strong alkali   pH 1

Neutral   pH 9

Strong acid   pH 7

Weak alkali   pH 5

Weak acid   pH 14

Acids and Alkalis

Q3 What is the name given to a dye that **changes colour** depending on whether it is in an acid or an alkali? Circle the correct answer.

Acid   Alkali   Indicator   Evaporate

Q4 Complete the table below, filling in the gaps with the words and numbers given.

8   strong acid   purple   blue   7

yellow   1   weak acid   13   neutral

Useful Substance	typical pH value	Colour with Universal Indicator	Acidic, Alkaline or Neutral
a) Hydrochloric acid in stomach		red	
b) Rain water	5		
c) Sodium hydroxide (oven cleaner)			strong alkali
d) Tap water		green	
e) Washing up liquid			weak alkali

Q5 Tick the box next to each true sentence below.

☐ Litmus paper is an indicator.

☐ Universal indicator can be used to work out the pH of a solution.

☐ Citric acid is a stronger acid than hydrochloric acid.

☐ Citric acid is a stronger acid than rain water.

Neutralisation Reactions

Q1 Tick the correct box to show whether each sentence is **true** or **false**.

	True	False
a) All neutralisation reactions produce the same salt.	☐	☐
b) The name of the salt produced by neutralisation depends on the acid.	☐	☐
c) Water can be removed from a salt solution by evaporation.	☐	☐
d) Neutralisation reactions produce salt, water and oxygen.	☐	☐

Q2 An acid and an alkali will react to make a **salt** and **water**.

a) Write a word equation for this reaction.

....

b) What is the name given to this type of reaction? Circle the correct answer.

combustion	thermal decomposition	neutralisation

c) What is the pH of the salt and water produced in this reaction?

....

Q3 Different acids react with alkalis to form **different salts**. Draw lines to match the salts on the left to the acids that could make them on the right.

Sodium sulfate

Hint: Look at the last word of each salt name.

Calcium chloride

Calcium sulfate

Hydrochloric acid

Magnesium sulfate

Sulfuric acid

Potassium chloride

Neutralisation Reactions

Q4 Lucy is making a salt by **neutralising** sodium hydroxide with hydrochloric acid.

a) i) The steps she must follow are written below, but they are in the wrong order. Write the numbers **1-6** in the boxes to show the order the steps should be done in. Step 5 has been done for you.

☐ Repeat the last two steps until you have a neutral solution.

☐ Take a small sample of the solution in the test tube to see if the pH is neutral.

☐ Fill a test tube with 20 cm³ of sodium hydroxide.

☐ Leave the solution over night to form nice big salt crystals.

☐ Add a few drops of hydrochloric acid to the test tube.

5 Add the solution to a dish and boil off some of the liquid so you're left with a concentrated solution.

ii) What liquid is boiled off in **step 5**?

....

b) Acids and alkalis can be **harmful**. Suggest one way Lucy can help protect herself when doing this experiment.

....

c) Complete the word equation below.

hydrochloric acid + sodium hydroxide → .... + water

Reactivity Series and Metal Extraction

Q1   Write the numbers **1-6** in the boxes to put the metals
below in order from **most reactive** (1) to **least reactive** (6).

☐ magnesium   ☐ potassium   ☐ copper

☐ iron   ☐ aluminium   ☐ zinc

Q2   How easy it is to **extract** a metal from its ore depends on how reactive it is.

a)   Draw lines to match up the following metals to their **method of extraction**.

lead   electricity

potassium   reduced by carbon

magnesium   electricity

b)   Complete the sentence below.

> A metal can be extracted from its ore using carbon if
> it is .... reactive than carbon.

Q3   This question is about metal extraction.

a)   Tick (✔) the statement that is **true** about metal extraction.

☐   Sodium can be extracted from its ore using carbon.

☐   The process of extracting a metal from its ore using carbon is called reduction.

☐   Electricity is needed to extract copper from copper ore.

☐   Electricity is the only way to extract metals less reactive than carbon from their ores.

b)   Gold is normally found in its pure form and doesn't need extracting from an ore.
Why is gold usually found in its pure form?

....

Reactivity Series and Metal Extraction

Q4 Iron is found in the ground as **iron ore**. Iron is **extracted** from its ore using reduction by carbon in a **blast furnace**, like the one shown in the diagram.

Iron ore and carbon in

The carbon and iron ore react in the very hot blast furnace.

Molten iron out

a) What is meant by **reduction**? Circle the correct answer.

adding oxygen   adding iron   removing oxygen   removing iron

b) What are **ores**?

....

....

c) Iron ore is mostly made up of iron oxide. Complete the equation below showing how carbon and iron ore react. (Words to use: carbon, iron, dioxide, carbon.)

.... + iron oxide → .... + ...

d) Why can't aluminium be extracted from its ore using a blast furnace?

....

....

e) What would you use to extract aluminium from its ore?

....

Reaction of Metals with Acids

Q1   Below are the names of **seven** metals that react with an acid to make a salt and hydrogen. Circle the metals that will react **violently** with acid.

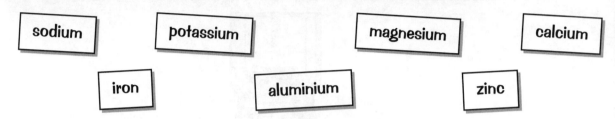

sodium   potassium   magnesium   calcium

iron   aluminium   zinc

Q2   A student set up **four** test tubes as shown below. She observed the reactions that happened. She also held a lit splint over each test tube, and recorded some of the things she saw and heard in the table **below**.

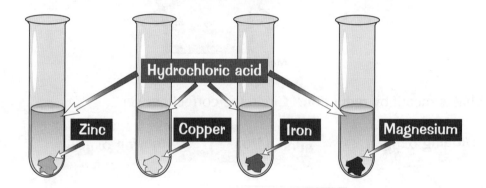

Hydrochloric acid

Zinc   Copper   Iron   Magnesium

a)   Complete the table by filling in what she should have observed.

Metal	Observations of reaction	Sound made by a lit splint above reaction
zinc		Squeaky pop
magnesium	Reacted violently	
iron	Reacted fairly well	Small squeaky pop
copper		No sound

b)   Which gas causes the squeaky pop?

....

Reaction of Metals with Acids

Q3   Joshua put some **aluminium** in a flask with some **hydrochloric acid**.
He collected the gas given off as shown in the diagram.

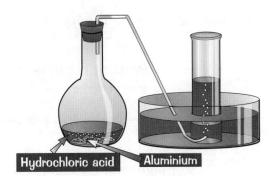

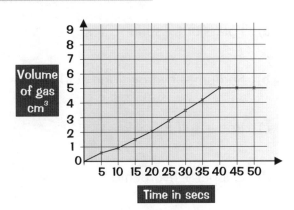

a)   He recorded the total volume of gas given off every 5 seconds and plotted the
results on the graph above. What volume of gas was produced after 50 seconds?

....

b)   Would the reaction be more or less violent if **calcium** metal was used instead of
aluminium? Explain your answer.

....

....

Q4   Damian's teacher reacted **potassium** with **hydrochloric acid**.
Damian knew that if they reacted they would make **potassium chloride**
and **hydrogen gas**, but he didn't know how violently they would react.

a)   Would potassium and hydrochloric acid react violently, fairly well or not at all?

....

b)   What would Damian hear when he held a lit
splint above the reaction if hydrogen gas was made?

....

c)   What type of substance is made when a metal reacts with an acid?
Circle the correct answer.

| A metal oxide | Water | A salt | An acid |

Reaction of Metals with Acids

Q5 Complete the chemical equations below by drawing lines between the correct **products** and **reactants**.

a) Potassium + sulfuric acid →

b) Sodium + hydrochloric acid →

c) Iron + sulfuric acid →

d) Copper + hydrochloric acid →

e) Magnesium + sulfuric acid →

> Iron sulfate + hydrogen

> Sodium chloride + hydrogen

> No reaction — metal too unreactive

> Magnesium sulfate + hydrogen

> Potassium sulfate + hydrogen

Q6 Fill in the spaces using the clues below and find the **mystery word**. The letters that make up the mystery word are in the shaded boxes.

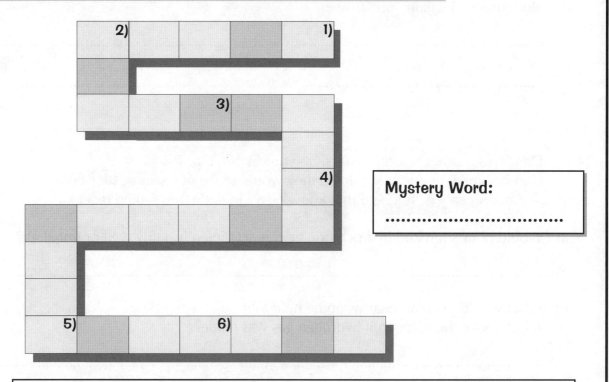

Mystery Word:

....

1. Reacts fairly well with hydrochloric acid to make iron chloride. (4)

2. This metal has the symbol Pb and reacts fairly well with acids. (4)

3. Hydrogen is displaced from this when you add a reactive metal. (4)

4. A very very very reactive metal. (9)

5. Hydrogen gas makes this noise near a lit splint. (3)

6. The metal that reacts with sulfuric acid to give zinc sulfate. (4)

Reactions of Oxides with Acids

Q1   Complete these chemical equations by writing the correct **products** after the arrows. Choose from the products shown below.

| carbon dioxide | water | aluminium hydroxide | aluminium oxide |

| hydrogen sulfate | iron hydroxide | iron oxide | oxygen carbonate |

a)   iron + oxygen → ....

b)   hydrogen + oxygen → ....

c)   aluminium + oxygen → ....

d)   carbon + oxygen → ....

Q2   Fill in the gaps in these word equations.

a)   silicon + ... → silicon dioxide

b)   .... + oxygen → potassium oxide

c)   sulfur + ... → .... dioxide

d)   .... + ... → lead oxide

Q3   **Lithium oxide** is mixed with water to make a solution.

a)   Is the solution an acid, an alkali or neutral?

....

b)   Which **salt** will be made if **hydrochloric acid** is added to the beaker?

....

c)   Name **one** other product of the reaction between lithium oxide and hydrochloric acid.

....

Reactions of Oxides with Acids

Q4   Tyler reacts phosphorus oxide with an alkali.

a)   What type of chemical is phosphorus oxide? Circle the correct answer.

A non-metal oxide   A metal oxide

b)   Is phosphorus oxide acidic, alkaline or neutral?

....

c)   What will be produced in this reaction? Circle the correct answer(s).

Water   An acid   A salt

Q5   Solve the clues and complete this crossword.

<u>Down</u>

1)   This reacts with oxygen to make an acidic oxide (3-5)

2)   One of the products of a reaction between an acid and a metal oxide (4)

3)   A solution that has a pH higher than 7 (6)

4)   A substance that makes sodium oxide when burned in oxygen (6)

<u>Across</u>

5)   .... oxides are alkaline (5)

6)   Metal oxides react with this to make a salt and water (4)

7)   This Group 1 element forms an alkaline oxide (7)

Displacement Reactions

Q1   David put **three** metals in test tubes filled with **copper sulfate** solution.

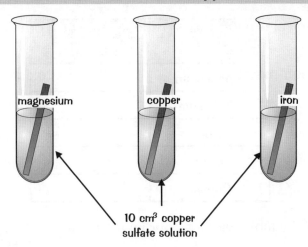

magnesium   copper   iron

10 cm³ copper
sulfate solution

a)   Complete the table to show which metal was **deposited** in each tube
    after half an hour. If no metal was deposited, write 'no deposit'.

Original metal	Deposited metal
Magnesium	
Copper	
Iron	

b) i)   Complete the equation to show what happened in one of the test tubes.

iron + copper sulfate → .... + ... sulfate

ii) What is the name for this type of reaction?

....

c)   Which is the least reactive metal in this experiment?

....

d)   If David put a piece of **silver** into another test tube of
    copper sulfate, what would he see? Explain your answer.

....

....

Displacement Reactions

Q2   The metals shown in the table were placed in a **zinc sulfate** solution.

Metal	Reaction with zinc sulfate
Magnesium	
Aluminium	
Iron	
Lead	
Copper	

a)   Fill in each row of the table with a tick (✔) if the metal reacted, or a cross (✘) if it didn't.

b)   What would **coat** the surface of the metals that reacted? Circle the correct answer.

magnesium   sulfur   zinc   sulfur dioxide   zinc oxide

Q3   Fill in the missing words using the clues below
and find the **mystery metal** in the shaded boxes.

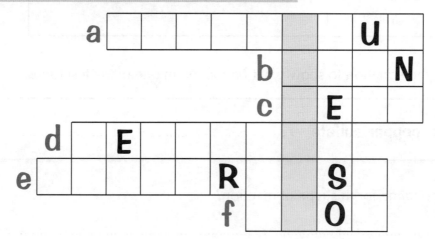

a)   A metal that's more reactive than aluminium, but less reactive than potassium.

b)   This is more reactive than copper.

c)   A metal less reactive than iron — but only just.

d)   Copper cannot displace zinc from zinc sulfate because it is not _____ enough.

e)   When magnesium is added to blue copper sulfate solution the liquid turns _____ .

f)   This would be seen coating the zinc strip in the reaction between zinc and iron sulfate.

The mystery metal is ....

Displacement Reactions

Q4 Hannah is investigating the reactivity of metal X compared to other metals. She put a piece of each metal shown in the table into a test tube of **iron sulfate** and left them for half an hour. The table below shows her results.

Metal	Reaction with iron sulfate
Magnesium	Iron deposited
Iron	No reaction
Copper	No reaction
Metal X	No reaction

a) Hannah tested metal X in **copper sulfate** solution. Copper was deposited. Fill in the blanks in this sentence about the reactivity of metal X.

Metal **X** is less reactive than ....

and more reactive than ....

b) What could metal X be?

....

c) Write the numbers **1-4** in the boxes below to put the metals in order from **most reactive** (1) to **least reactive** (4).

☐ iron   ☐ copper   ☐ magnesium   ☐ metal **X**

Q5 The symbol equation below shows the neutralisation of sodium hydroxide and hydrochloric acid. This is a **displacement** reaction.

$$NaOH + HCl \rightarrow NaCl + H_2O$$

Have a look at the periodic table if you need help remembering the symbol for each element.

a) Name the element that gets displaced in this reaction. ....

b) Name the element that displaces it. ....

The Earth's Structure

Q1   Here is a picture of the layers inside the Earth.

a)   Draw an arrow from each label to the correct layer of the Earth shown in the picture.

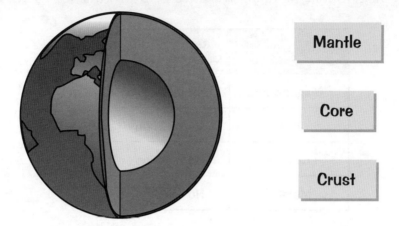

Mantle

Core

Crust

b)   Fill in the gaps in these sentences about the Earth's structure using the words in the boxes.

sphere   centre   crust   rock

The Earth is almost a .... and is made up of several layers.

The .... is a thin layer of solid ....

The core is at the .... of the Earth.

c)   Complete the sentence by **circling** the correct words in brackets.

The mantle is mostly (**solid / liquid**), but deep down it
can flow very (**quickly / slowly**) like a (**solid / liquid**).

d)   Write down which **layer** of the Earth each sentence is talking about.

i)   The part of the Earth that we live on.

....

ii) Scientists think this layer is made from iron and nickel.

....

The Earth's Structure

Q2   The Earth's crust is made up of **rocks**.

a)   Use the words in the box to fill in these gaps
to show what the rocks are made from.

compounds
elements minerals

Rocks ➡ .... ➡ .... and ....

b)   Give an example of a **mineral** found in the Earth's crust.

....

Q3   The picture below shows the **plates** that make up the Earths's surface.

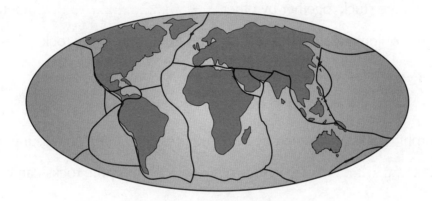

a)   Which layers of the Earth are the plates made from?

....

b)   The Earth's plates are **moving** all the time.

i) Why can the plates move?

....

ii) How fast do the plates normally move?

....

c)   Kazuki lives in Tokyo, Japan, close to where two plates meet.
Sometimes there are **earthquakes** in Tokyo. What causes earthquakes?

....

....

Rock Types

Q1 Here are some sentences about different **types of rock**. Put the following words in the gaps so that the sentences make sense.

> crystals   fossils   layers   long   magma
> millions   minerals   seas   three

There are .... different types of rock. Igneous rocks are

formed when melted underground rock called .... cools.

Sedimentary rocks are formed from layers of sediment laid down in lakes or

.... over .... of years. The particles

of sediment are stuck together by other .... Sometimes

the remains of long dead plants and animals are found in the rock. These are

called ....

Metamorphic rocks are formed by heat and pressure acting on existing rocks

over .... periods of time. Metamorphic rocks can contain

tiny .... and may also have ....

Q2 **Igneous** rocks can form in **two** different ways.

a) One way that they form is when magma cools quickly above the ground.
How does the magma get above the ground?

....

....

b) Describe the other way that igneous rocks can be **formed**.

....

....

Rock Types

Q3 Look at the descriptions of various rocks below. Try to identify each type of rock as **igneous (I)**, **sedimentary (S)** or **metamorphic (M)** by writing the correct letter in the box next to each rock.

Basalt
A dark rock with small crystals, formed on the surface of the Earth.

Chalk
A white rock formed from the shells of sea animals which collected at the bottom of shallow seas.

Slate
A dark rock showing crystals and layers. It was formed by shale being changed by heat and pressure.

Grit
Rock formed from small particles stuck together.

Granite
A speckled rock formed from melted rock which cooled slowly inside the earth.

Marble
A white rock made from crystals that also shows layers. It is formed from chalk or limestone by heat and pressure.

Obsidian
A glassy rock formed by volcanoes.

Sandstone
A rock formed from small grains of sand which have been squeezed tightly together.

Quartzite
A rock with crystals which has been formed by changes due to heat and pressure within the earth.

Rock Types

Q4 Sandra went to a quarry and drew this sketch of a **rock face**. The rock face has six different types of rock, labelled 1-6. Her teacher told her that all the rocks apart from rock 6 are **sedimentary**.

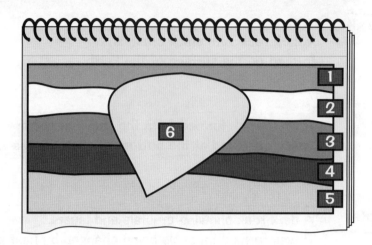

a) How are **sedimentary** rocks formed?

....

....

....

b) Her teacher told her that rock 6 is an **igneous** rock that did **not** come from magma from a volcano. Describe how this rock was formed.

....

....

....

I liked igneous rocks before they were cool...

....

c) Over millions of years, layers of sedimentary rocks can be changed into a different type of rock. What is the name of this kind of rock?

....

d) What **two** things cause sedimentary rock to change into the type of rock in part **c**).

1. ....

2. ....

The Rock Cycle

Q1   These parts of the **rock cycle** have got all scrambled up. Use the descriptions to help you unscramble them, and write the unscrambled words in the table.

Scrambled word	Description	Word
a) FIPTUL	Rocks are pushed up to the surface.	
b) TEMGLIN	Lots of heat changes solid rock into magma.	
c) GOLOCNI	The molten rock turns solid to form igneous rock.	
d) SOENIOR	Wearing down rocks, for example, by rain.	
e) OXRUSEPE	When rocks are visible on the Earth's surface.	
f) THAE and RUSPEERS	Squashing and heating turns rocks into metamorphic rocks.	
g) GAWTNIREHE	Breaking down rock into smaller bits.	
h) PEDSIOTNIO	Laying down sediment.	
i) LARIBU and SNERPMOCSIO	Squeezing and compressing layers of sediment.	
j) STNARTNOIPROAT	Moving bits of eroded rock about by wind and water.	

Q2   Tick the boxes to show whether these statements about the rock cycle are **true** or **false**.

		True	False
a)	Igneous rocks change into sedimentary rocks.	☐	☐
b)	Sedimentary rocks are formed by the weathering of other rocks.	☐	☐
c)	The rock cycle takes millions of years to complete.	☐	☐
d)	Magma forms igneous rocks when it cools.	☐	☐
e)	Burial of sediment makes igneous rocks.	☐	☐
f)	When rocks are exposed, they start to be eroded, and the cycle starts again.	☐	☐
g)	Exposure happens inside the Earth.	☐	☐

The Rock Cycle

Q3 The diagram below is a simplified picture of the **rock cycle**. The numbers represent **rock types** and **processes**. Write the numbers in the correct place in the table below.

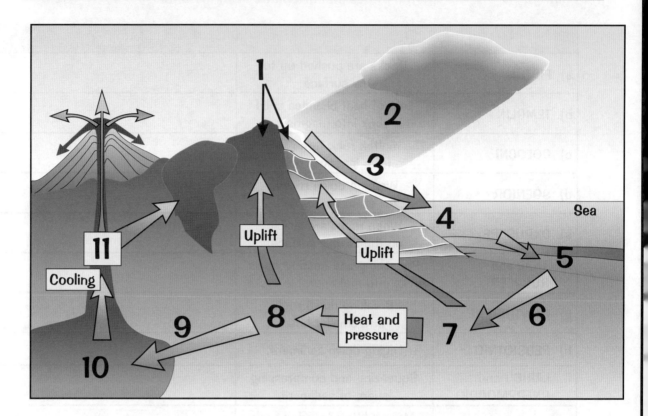

Label	Number
Sedimentary rocks	
Metamorphic rocks	
Sediments	
Magma	
Weathering	
Erosion and transport	
Igneous rock	
Deposition	
Exposure	
Melting	
Burial and compression	

Recycling

Q1 Humans use **fossil fuels** to make many useful products.

a) Put a tick (✔) next to all the things that are **made** from fossil fuels.

Plastic bags ☐   Petrol ☐   Metal screws ☐

Pencils ☐   Wooden chairs ☐   Plastic cups ☐

b) Fill in the gaps in the passage with the words in the boxes below.

| limited | long | millions of years | crude oil | plants |

Millions of years ago, dead .... and animals were buried in the Earth's crust. Over time, they turned into fossil fuels like ....

Fossil fuels are .... resources because they take such a .... time to make. Once all the fossil fuels have been used, we won't get any more for ....

Q2 Humans need to try to **recycle** materials as much as possible.

a) What does recycling mean?

....

....

b) Write down **three** reasons why recycling is **better** than making new things all the time.

1. ....

....

2. ....

....

3. ....

....

Recycling

Q3   Barry wants to open a factory that makes **aluminium cans**.
He's trying to decide if he should get the metal from old cans
that have been **recycled**, or **brand new** aluminium.

a)   Use the words in the boxes to fill in the gaps in these sentences.

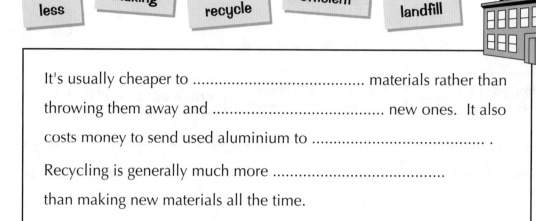

less   making   recycle   efficient   landfill

Barry's Cans
"Yes, We Can"

It's usually cheaper to .... materials rather than

throwing them away and .... new ones. It also

costs money to send used aluminium to ....

Recycling is generally much more ....

than making new materials all the time.

b)   Brand new metals have to be extracted from rocks that have been mined from the
ground. What are these rocks containing metals called?

....

c)   Barry wants to use whichever aluminium is best for the environment.

i)   Producing aluminium always uses energy.
Circle a reason why using more energy is a problem.

Energy will run
out faster.

Fossil fuels will
run out faster.

The Sun will
run out faster.

ii) Which aluminium uses less energy to make — recycled or brand new aluminium?
Explain your answer.

....

....

....

iii) Should Barry choose to make his cans from recycled aluminium or new aluminium?

....

The Carbon Cycle

Q1 **Carbon dioxide** is a gas in the Earth's atmosphere.

a) Complete the paragraph below using the words in the boxes.

| living | used up | environment | recycled |

Carbon is a part of all .... things. It is never ....,
just .... It constantly passes between living things before being
returned to the ....

b) What is the name of the **process** that removes carbon dioxide from the air?

....

c) Circle the **organism** that uses this process to take carbon dioxide out of the air.

Frogs   Plants   Insects

Humans   Badgers

Q2 All plants and animals **respire**.

a) Carbon is released into the air as a gas during **respiration**. What is the name of the gas?

....

b) i) What do **decomposers** do to waste and dead organisms?

....

ii) Describe how decomposers release carbon back into the air.

....

....

c) **Fossil fuels** contain carbon. How do **humans** release the carbon in fossil fuels back into the air?

....

The Carbon Cycle

Q3   The diagram below shows part of a food chain.

a)   Draw an arrow to show which direction **carbon** is passed between the lamb and the grass below.

grass   lamb

b)   How is carbon passed between organisms in the food chain above?

....

....

Q4   Complete the table below by matching the numbers **1-7** from the diagram of the carbon cycle below to the correct words in the table.

Label	Number
Combustion	
Respiration (decomposers)	
Decomposers	
Photosynthesis	
Respiration (plants and animals)	
Fossil fuels	
Eating	

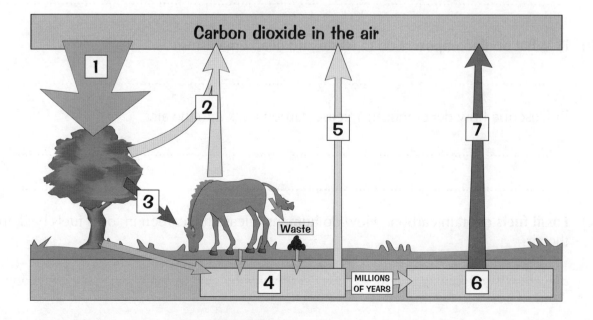

The Atmosphere and Climate

Q1 The pie chart below shows the percentages of different gases that make up the **atmosphere**.

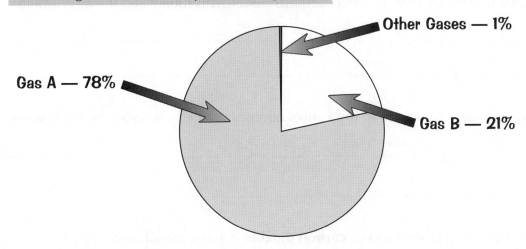

a) What are gases A and B?

Gas A — ....

Gas B — ....

b) One of the other gases labelled in the pie chart is carbon dioxide.

    i) Roughly what **percentage** of the atmosphere is carbon dioxide?

    ....

    ii) Name **one** other gas that makes up the Earth's atmosphere.

    ....

Q2 Many parts of the Amazon rainforest are being **deforested** to make room for farming.

a) What is **deforestation**?

....

b) Complete the sentences below by circling the correct word in brackets.

> Deforestation causes an (**increase** / **decrease**) in carbon dioxide in the
>
> atmosphere. This is because there is (**more** / **less**) photosynthesis, so
>
> (**more** / **less**) carbon dioxide is removed from the atmosphere.

The Atmosphere and Climate

Q3 When humans burn fossil fuels, carbon dioxide is **released** into the atmosphere.

a) Write down **two** examples of when humans burn fossils fuels.

1. ....

2. ....

b) Explain how carbon dioxide in the Earth's atmosphere helps to keep the Earth **warm**.

....

....

c) What's happening to the level of **carbon dioxide** in the atmosphere?
Circle the correct answer.

It's increasing   It's decreasing   It's staying the same

Q4 The Earth's temperature is gradually increasing.

a) What name is given to this effect?

....

b) What is causing this effect?

....

....

c) Name **two** effects that this effect could have, and explain why each would be bad.

Effect: ....

Explanation: ....

....

Effect: ....

Explanation: ....

....